Michael Johnstone

Mountains

CHARTWELL BOOKS INC.

Designed and produced by
Albany Books
36 Park Street London W1Y 4DE

First published 1979

Published by Chartwell Books Inc.
A Division of Book Sales Inc.
110 Enterprise Avenue
Secaucus, New Jersey 07094

Copyright © Albany Books 1979

Printed in Hong Kong

Design: Nicholas Newton
Picture research: Mary Corcoran

Contents

Introduction

Left: *The Flinders Range in Australia is one of the most curious fold ranges. The system of domes and basins resulted from intense pressure from every side. (Spectrum Colour Library)*

Below: *Hannibal and his armies cross the Alps in one of the most staggeringly successful military operations of all time. (Mary Evans Picture Library)*

To the ancient Greeks, mountains were sacred. They were the homes of the Gods, presided over by Zeus, who occasionally visited the plains in one form or another and around whom an entire mythology was established.

Mountains were important in the story of the Old Testament. It was in the mountains that Moses received the Ten Commandments and it was on a mountain top that the Ark came to rest.

To Hannibal, mountains were an obstacle that had to be crossed to ensure the success of his military campaigns.

Two thousand years later, on the eve of the coronation of Queen Elizabeth II of Great Britain, the whole world was thrilled to learn that Everest, the highest mountain in the world, had been climbed.

What is it about mountains that has inspired mythologies and majestic feats of bravery?

Why have men and women risked life and limb to climb them?

The best answer to these questions is the most common one — because they are there.

But how did they get there?
The earth's crust is said to be made up of several plates. These are blocks which, over periods of millions of years, move away from and towards each other. When two plates come together, one tries to force its way on top of the other

HENRI MOTTE. 1878

and when this happens the land on the edge of the upper plate is thrust up in great folds. Mountains formed by such movements of the earth's crust are said to be *fold mountains*.

The Himalayas were so formed about 50 million years ago and they are considered to be young mountains. It is precisely because they are so young (in terms of the age of the earth) that they are so high. Erosion and weather have not yet worn and smoothed them, and reduced them in size as they have the Urals in the USSR, the Great Dividing Range of Australia and the Highlands of Scotland. These mountain ranges and areas were formed 50 million years before the Himalayas!

Many of the individual peaks that are not part of ranges are the result of volcanic action. Beneath the surface of the earth's crust there is an inconceivably hot mass of molten matter. Occasionally it forces its way through weak points in the crust of the earth. This is how mountains such as Kilimanjaro in Tanzania were formed.

As well as moving horizontally, the crust of the earth also moves vertically along natural cracks. Occasionally, millions of years ago, huge blocks of crust were tilted upwards along a fault and formed what are known as *block mountains*. The Sierra Nevada of California in the United States is an example of this.

Although the world's mountains were formed long before man came on the scene and present an often forbidding, indomitable appearance, man has learned to climb them, to use them for pasture, to tap their fast flowing waters to generate electricity, and to ski down their snow-covered slopes. They have become man's friends but maintain their staunch independence. They were there before we were and will be there after we have gone.

Right: *The highest mountain in the world, Mount Everest, was first climbed in 1953, more than 30 years after the first attempt was made. (ZEFA, H. Weyer)*

Below: *Mount Ngaruahde is a typical volcano. It is situated in the North Island of New Zealand, and its smooth sides and flattened top are similar to those of the other volcanic mountains of the world. Ngaruahde is still active. (ZEFA, G. Riethmaier)*

Right: *Skiing down snow-covered mountain slopes has become one of the most popular participant sports over the past few years. Cheaper air travel and package holidays have made skiing accessible to people living hundreds of miles away from the slopes. (ZEFA, K. Bammer)*

Opposite: *The Black Hills of South Dakota are dome mountains, formed by huge blocks of rock being thrust upwards along natural faults in the Earth's crust. (ZEFA, H. Steenmans)*

Mountain making

The formation of mountains involves two processes — orogeny and epeirogeny. Orogeny is the contraction and compression of a mobile zone of the earth's crust. Epeirogeny is the uplifting of part of the crust. Both happen because of intense activity in the centre of the earth. Do not imagine that the earth's contours have settled into their final form — mountain building is still going on. The earthquakes and volcanoes which we read about show that the earth is in a state of continual flux and millions of years from now new mountain ranges may well have formed, and the ones with which we are familiar today will have been smoothed and reduced in size by the wind and erosion.

Geologists have established that there have been several intense periods of mountain building in the evolution of our planet. The earliest occurred 570,000,000 years ago during pre-Cambrian times. After that things seem to have quietened down until about 225,000,000 years ago when, during the Paleozoic period there was renewed activity and again during the Cretaceous period about 100,000,000 years ago.

During these periods the rate of uplift expansion was probably little more than a few millimetres each year, but over periods of millions of years vast mountain ranges can be formed.

There are, as we saw earlier, several different types of mountains: dome, block and fold mountains, volcanoes, alpine-type mountains, and residual mountains.

Dome mountains

The Black Hills of South Dakota in the United States are an example of dome mountains which were formed by pressure that forced parts of the surface upwards, without causing fractures.

Right: *Mount Fuji, in Japan. Because it is sacred to the Shinto religion, women were forbidden from its slopes until 100 years ago. (ZEFA)*

Below: *This mountain in the Jura shows a typical fold shape and structure. (ZEFA, D. H. Teuffen)*

Thus, dome mountains are relatively flat and smooth with gradual slopes rather than ruggedly grand like the Himalayas.

Block mountains

Mountains which rise abruptly out of the landscape were probably formed by forces that caused huge blocks to be forced upwards along natural linear faults. Such mountains are block mountains. The Canadians have a superb example of them in the Laurentian mountains in southern Quebec which are the oldest in the North American Continent and which the Canadians refer to as the oldest mountains in the world.

Fold mountains

The Swiss Jura is a classic example of a fold mountain range, with straight parallel valleys and ridges carved out of the rock. They were formed by compression and uplift of sedimentary rocks which lie on a granite base. The strong granite reacts to the pressure in a different way to the softer sedimentary rocks, but when the pressure is so intense that the granite base breaks into fault wedges and the softer sedimentary rocks are folded into parallel folds, we have *fold fault mountains* such as the Andean Cordillera Oriental.

Volcanoes

The most spectacular mountain building process is seen in volcanoes which erupt in unbelievable displays of pyrotechnics. Volcanoes are formed by the upthrust of lava from the molten centre of the earth. Where the lava flows from one central point, the result is the classic dome-shaped volcanic mountains such as Fuji in Japan (which, incidentally, last erupted in 1707). This conical shape can be eroded by explosion giving a less dramatic silhouette, such as Krakatoa which erupted with incredible fury in 1883, an explosion that killed

The Kilauea Jki crater in Hawaii, with Mauna Loa in the background. (Spectrum Colour Library)

thousands of people and which was heard thousands of miles away. Where the lava flows from fissures rather than one central point, the mountain is said to be a *broad-shield volcano*. Mauna Loa in Hawaii is such a volcano. If we counted the height of mountains from their base below land, Mauna Loa would be the highest in the world as it rises from 18,000 feet (5486m) below the sea and stretches 13,000 feet (3962m) above it. Its total height would be something over 32,000 feet (9753m) dwarfing Everest by 4000 feet (1219m)!

Alpine-type mountains

Complex belts of folded and faulted rocks are said to be Alpine-type mountains. Obviously the Alps are an example of such mountains, so too are the North American Cordillera.

Alpine-type mountains arose from mobile belts of oceanic sediments called geosynclines. These are subdivided into two zones — myogeosynclines which adjoin a continental platform and eugeosynclines which are further from a continent. Myogeosyncline is an accumulation of sandstone and limestone whereas eugeosyncline is much more variable, comprising shales, siltstones and impure sandstones. Generally, the exterior belt of Alpine-type mountains is composed of myogeosynclinal rocks and the interior is composed of the other.

Alpine-type belts evolved in two ways: at the boundary between a continent and an ocean and at the point of contact of two continental masses. In the former, folding occurs where the oceanic crust is pushed below the continental margin and in the latter, folding is due to contraction of a former ocean and collision between the two bordering continents.

The main valleys of Alpine-type mountain systems follow the later faults and warps and this can be seen especially well in the Rocky Mountains of the Northern American continent. Sharp ridges rise from the valleys and where several ridges meet, steep peaks are found. One of the steepest in North America is the highest mountain in the United States outside Alaska — Mount Whitney. At 14,495 feet(4400m) it is situated in the Sierra Nevada of eastern California. With steep slopes in the east, it rises abruptly for 11,000 feet (3352m) from the Owens Valley.

Residual mountains

Mountains which are remnants of any mountain type which have been eroded by time are said to be *residual mountains*. Much of the southern Appalachians of the United States are residual.

Formation

Alpine-type mountains and fold mountains are produced by compression and subsequent uplift. Dome and block mountains are formed by vertical movement and slight extension or separation of the earth's crust. Alpine-type mountains originated at the continental end during an orogeny and their oceanic counterparts are known as island arcs. Fold mountains form on continental platforms where segments of the continent have yielded to the forces transmitted from adjoining Alpine belts.

Mountain systems

The largest mountain system in the world is the circum-Pacific system which consists of three segments — the North American Cordillera and the mountain belts of eastern Siberia, the South American Cordillera, and the west Pacific arcs.

The North American Cordillera is dominated by two Alpine belts of the late Mesozoic and Cenozoic ages (around 65,000,000 years ago). They make up the higher ranges of the east and west and are separated by a plateau, basins and smaller ranges. The central part of the Cordillera was influenced by severe folding that took place in the Paleozoic

19

era but by the Middle Tertiary times (30,000,000 years ago) the folding was essentially finished. During the last 7,000,000 years volcanic rocks erupted in the central zone and these now cover part of Oregon, Washington and Mexico.

The east Siberian belts also consist of two Alpine belts — the Continental and the Pacific. The former comprises the mountains of Verhoyansk and the latter comprises the ranges from Anadyr to Kamchatka.

The South American Cordilleras are made up of one mountain chain stretching down the coast of South America. Formed during the Triassic, Jurassic and early Cretaceous periods, the rocks of the Andes were warped,

faulted and thrusted during the late Cretaceous and early Tertiary eras. Many volcanic peaks are found in the Andes due to the underthrusting of the crust of the Pacific.

The western Pacific is framed by two sets of island arcs. The outer arc comprises the Aleutan, Kuril-Kamchatka and Bonnin-Mariana arcs, the Bismark Archipelago and Solomon Islands, the Tonga-Kermadec Arc and New Zealand. New Zealand consists of two major islands and several smaller ones. The North Island is 44,300 square miles (114,740 sq. km) and has several active volcanic craters. South Island is crossed lengthwise by an Alpine range of jagged peaks and glaciers. Mount Cook (12,349 ft/3766m) overlooks the ruggest west

Opposite: *The Alpine chain. (RIDA, R. C. L. Wilson)*

Below: *The Milford Sound in the South Island of New Zealand, clearly showing the Alpine structure of the mountains in the background. (ZEFA, R. Halin)*

coast of South Island. New Zealand is typical of the outer arc of the western Pacific in that it is underlain with Paleozoic and Mesozoic stones and rocks that were folded during Triassic and Tertiary times.

The inner system of the arc extends from Sakhalin to Japan to Ryukyu, through the Philippines arc where it joins one of the other great mountain systems, the Tethyan system.

This system rose from a wide sea named the Tethys. It began to form around 280,000,000 years ago and separates the continental platforms of Eurasia from Africa and India. In the west it consists of two continuous belts: the northern belt comprises the Betic Cordillera, the Alps, the Carpathians, Balkan Mountains, Caucasus and Elburz ranges; the southern belt contains the Tell Atlas, Appenines, the mountains of Greece and Yugoslavia, the Hungarian Basin, the mountains of Northern Turkey and the plateaus of Iran and Afghanistan.

During the last 7,000,000 years the mountain ranges were uplifted and eroded creating the formidable peaks that we know today.

Other mountain systems are the block-faulted uplifts of Western Europe which are underlain by Precambrian and Paleozoic rocks that were folded during the late Paleozoic period, eroded during Permian times and uplifted during the Mesozoic and Cenozoic; the platform areas of North and South America, Africa, India and Australia which were eroded during the early Mesozoic and then upwarped during the past 7,000,000 years; the basin and range areas of the United States which are characterized by uplifted fault blocks; and the basin and range areas of Siberia, Mongolia, Sinkiang, Tibet and China where some of the highest mountain ranges in the world are found.

Right: *An aerial view of part of the Andes. (Spectrum Colour Library)*

Below: *Mount Aragats in the Lesser Caucasus is typical of the peaks in the Tethyan system. It is 13,435 feet (4095m) high. (ZEFA, Heinrich)*

The mountain
ranges of the world

Mount Everest

To include all the world's mountains and mountain ranges in one volume would be an almost impossible task. One could start with the Aberdare Range in west central Kenya and work through alphabetically to the Zargos system of southwest Iran where some of the peaks rise to 15,000 feet (4572 m).

But let us start at the top, with the highest, and perhaps the most famous of all mountains — Everest. Everest is one of the peaks of the Himalayan Range that forms the border between Nepal and Tibet (now part of Chinese territory) in southern Asia. Its height was estimated at 29,002 feet (8839m) in 1852, but it is now accepted to be 29,154 feet (8884m). Before 1852 Chimbarazo in the Ecuadorian Andes was believed to be the highest mountain with an altitude of 20,577 feet (6272m).

Everest had been called Peak XV by European surveyors, but the local population had a much more attractive name for it — *Chomo Langma* which means Goddess Mother of the Snows. It had long been regarded by Tibetan and Nepalese Buddhists as a holy mountain. Indeed, two monasteries had been constructed in the Himalayas in such a way that the mountain dominated the skyline and the monks could spend as much time as possible contemplating their mother goddess.

As soon as news of Everest's height spread across the western world, mountaineers and explorers began to plan expeditions to climb it; but because of Nepal and Tibet objecting on religious and political grounds it was not until 1921 that permission was granted to an expedition sponsored by the Royal Geographical Society of Great Britain and the Alpine Club to make an assault on Everest.

The first task was to find a route to the mountain itself. This proved so exhausting that one member of the party died before the group had reached the mountain. The expedition eventually came back with a great deal of valuable information regarding the effects of high altitude on human beings; about the weather conditions and the route that they regarded as the most likely way of reaching the summit — along the north ridge.

Because Nepal was closed to foreigners, it was from Tibet that all expeditions set out to climb Everest. In 1922 a height of 27,000 feet (8229m) was reached by George Finch and Geoffrey Bruce. Two years later, Colonel Norton climbed to 28,140 feet (8961m) *without oxygen.*

One man who was determined to reach the summit with a single-mindedness that 'bordered on religious fanaticism' was an Englishman, George Leigh-Mallory. By 1924 the British expeditions had established camps up to a height of 26,000 feet (7924 m). Such camps are established in safe places out of the danger of avalanche after each day's climb. Food, clothing, oxygen, and so on are stored here.

In June of 1924 Leigh-Mallory and his companion, Irvine, set out from a camp that they had established at 26,440 feet (8057 m). Shortly after they set out into the mists, the clouds parted and they were spotted from 25,500 feet (7315 m) by another member of the expedition who was climbing up to the top camp with provisions. That was the last time Mallory and Irvine were to be seen. Their deaths remain the secret of the mountain.

Future expeditions of 1933, 1935, 1936 and 1938 all failed to mount the last hurdle — the final 800 feet (242m) to the summit.

In 1952, Eric Shipton decided to try a different approach along the edge of an inner recess on the southwest flank of the mountain, known as West Cwm. Shipton failed to reach the summit as did a Swiss expedition which set out later in the same year.

In 1953 a group of men led by John (later Lord) Hunt set out to try to conquer the mountain. Members of the group were George Band, Thomas Bourdillon, Thomas Evans, Alfred Gregory, Edmund Hillary, George Lowe, Wilfred Noyce, Griffeth Pugh, Thomas Stobbart, Sherpa Tenzing, Michael Ward, Michael Westmacott

Its local name is Chomo Langma, *but it is known throughout the world as Mount Everest — the highest of all the mountains in the world. (RIDA, D. J. Taylor)*

and Charles Wyll. History will probably remember the names of Hunt, and the two men who actually stood on the summit of the mountain — Hillary and Tenzing.

Hillary and Tenzing spent fifteen minutes on the top of the world's tallest mountain, fastening pennants of the three participating nations and giving thanks to their gods. Hillary dug a small hole in the snow and buried a cross that had been given to him. Tenzing buried some chocolate, sugar and biscuits under the snow — offerings to the gods who had guarded the roof of the world for centuries and who had now given up their secrets.

Since then, many successful attempts have been made on Everest, but the mountain has not surrendered completely. Many skilled mountaineers have lost their lives on the snow and ice-bound slopes of Everest in attempting to emulate the feat of the 1953 expedition.

The Himalayas

Everest is, of course, only one of the peaks in the Himalayas. The range is categorized into three distinct groups. The Greater Himalayas contain peaks averaging over 20,000 feet (6096m); the Lesser Himalayas range from 7000 feet

(2133m) to 15,000 feet (5572m); and the Outer Himalayas are, on average, below 5000 feet (1524m).

It is at the Himalayas that the masses of air from the Steppes of Central Asia meet the air from the low plains of the borders of the Indian Ocean. This causes tremendous atmospheric chaos. In summer, the monsoon drives moist air across the land. When this air meets the barrier of the Himalayas, the moisture falls as fresh snow on top of the deep winter's snow that lies thick until April. The monsoon begins in June and so there are only about eight weeks in which it is 'safe' to explore the Himalayas. Considering the shortness of this season it is surprising how much knowledge we have built up about the range. There are fifteen peaks over 26,000 feet (7924m). These are:

Everest   29,154 feet (8886m)
K2   28,250 feet (8610m)
Kanchenjunga   28,208 feet (8598m)
Lhotse   27,923 feet (8511m)
Makalu   27,824 feet (8481m)
Dhaulagiri   26,810 feet (8172m)
Manaslu   26,760 feet (8156m)
Cho Oyu   26,750 feet (8153m)
Nanga Parbat   26,660 feet (8126m)
Annapurna I   26,502 feet (8078m)
Gasherbrum I   26,470 feet (8068m)
Chogolisa   26,402 feet (8048m)
Gasherbrum II   26,360 feet (8035m)
Shisha Pangma   26,290 feet (8013m)
Annapurna II   26,041 feet (7937m)

All of them have now been conquered, one of them without anyone actually standing on the summit! This was *Kanchenjunga* which is considered to be

Right: *Lhotse is the fourth highest mountain in the world. It is situated on the Tibet-Nepal border in the southern Mount Everest massif. It was originally thought to be one of the peaks of Everest itself. (Spectrum Colour Library)*

Below: *Makalu is to the east of Everest and is sometimes known as the Armchair Peak because of its formation. It is so high that it is often shrouded in clouds. (ZEFA, Dr W. Loewe)*

Left: *Mount Ama Dublam lies in the Nepal Himalayas. (Spectrum Colour Library)*

Below: *Although it is considerably smaller than many other Himalayan peaks, Jobo Lhapshan (21,330ft/6500m) is still an impressive sight. (RIDA, D. J. Taylor)*

a holy mountain. Permission was only granted on the condition that the highest point of the peak was not to be touched by man. The British party honoured their agreement and climbed all except the last five feet (1½ m) of the mountain. Thus, although it had been officially conquered, no one had actually stood on the summit of Kanchenjunga. That was in 1955.

The first of the over-26,000 feet (7924m) mountains to be conquered was *Annapurna I* in June 1950 by a party of French mountaineers. Everest was climbed in 1953 and later in the same year *Nanga Parbat* succumbed to a lone Tyrollean climber, Herman Buhl, who climbed the last 4000 feet (1216 m) in sixteen-and-a-half hours without breathing apparatus. An Italian group climbed *K2* in 1954 and several weeks later *Cho Oyu* was conquered by an Austrian expedition.

The French got to the top of *Makalu* in 1955, in the same year that the British tackled Kanchenjunga. 1956 saw the Japanese on top of *Manaslu*, the Swiss astride the summit of *Lhotse* and the Austrians scaling *Gasherbrum II*. The following year gave the Austrians the chance to tackle *Chogolisa* and in 1958 an American expedition climbed *Gasherbrum I*. In 1960 a Swiss-led party conquered *Dhaulagiri* and four years later the last of the world's giant mountains was conquered when the Chinese scaled *Shisha Pangma*.

The Himalayan range stretches almost as far as from London to Athens, covering three longitudinal zones and

Left: *A typical Himalayan glacier in Kashmir. (RIDA, H. Boxer)*

varying in width from 100 miles (160km) to 150 miles (240km). On the south they rise up from a series of small foothills and on the north they drop sharply into the plateau of Tibet. Between the Indus and Sutlez rivers they are referred to as the *Punjab Himalayas*. They become the *Kamaun Himalayas* between the Sutlej and the Sarda. From the Sarda to the Tista they are the *Nepal Himalayas* and from there to the Brahmaputra they are the *Assam Himalayas*.

The range contains the longest glaciers outside the polar regions and even today much of the range is comparatively unknown. As recently as 1943 an American pilot reported that his altimeter was showing 32,000 feet (9754m) as he approached one Himalayan peak. Seventeen years later it was shown that his instrumentation must have been faulty when the peak was scaled by the Chinese who reported that the height was a mere 23,280 feet (7075m). But the fact that credence was given to the pilot's story could indicate that the Himalayas may not yet have given up all their secrets; and who knows, perhaps in some uncharted region there is a mountain of even greater height than Everest.

Cairngorm Mountains

At the other end of the scale, with an average height of 3000 feet (914m), thousands of miles away but geologically related to the Himalayas are the Cairngorms of northern Scotland. Both ranges are fold mountains, formed by movements in the plates of the earth's crust coming together with one plate forcing its way on top of the other.

The Cairngorms extend east to west between the upper valleys of the rivers Spey and Don. Several, but not many, of the peaks rise to over 4000 feet (1216m). On a fine spring day the weather

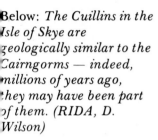

Below: *The Cuillins in the Isle of Skye are geologically similar to the Cairngorms — indeed, millions of years ago, they may have been part of them. (RIDA, D. Wilson)*

conditions make the mountains appear friendly and inviting, tempting amateur hill walkers to wander further than their equipment permits them to. Within minutes, conditions can change. Arctic blizzards can rage across the land, turning a pleasant spring walk into a frozen nightmare. Hardly a year passes without the Cairngorms claiming a life or two and the local mountain rescue service being called out many times. Even experienced Alpinists tread warily in these mountains. The height and situation of the Cairngorms give them an Arctic/Alpine wildlife that is unique in Britain.

The range is said to be stony and has given its name to a semi-precious gem that is found there. Occasionally the slopes break into fine, high granite cliffs which have become a popular challenge to experienced mountaineers, as has *Lochnagar,* one of the stiffest tests of mountaineering skills to be found in Britain. The Cairngorms also offer the finest skiing in the British Isles. This has recently been exploited and a booming tourist industry has grown around the once-sleepy Highland village of Aviemore. Every week while there is snow on the ground, the slopes of the Cairngorms are packed with winter sports enthusiasts. As well as a boom in tourism, this has also led to a sharp increase in the number of cases of cracked ribs and broken limbs that local doctors are called upon to care for.

The Alps

The Alpine range is the greatest mountain system in Europe, extending from the Gulf of Genoa more than 600 miles (960km) through Italy, France, Switzerland, Austria and Yugoslavia. The highest peak is Mont Blanc which rises to 15,781 feet (4786m).

The range is split into several groups. The *Maritime Alps* of the southwest spread northward into the *Cottian Alps* and the *Dauphine Alps.* These merge with the *Massif de Pelvoux* into the *Graian Alps* which narrow into the *Pennine Alps* of Northern Italy. North

The French Alps.
(Spectrum Colour
Library)

of the Pennine Alps is the Chain of *Mont Blanc* and the *Bernese Oberland.* These push their way into the *Lepontine Alps* which contain the famous *St Gotthard Pass.* East of the Lepontines are the *Albula Alps* which lie slightly to the north of the *Bernese Alps.* East of here are the *Dolomites* which merge with the *Julian Alps* on the north of the Adriatic Gulf.

The Alps contain many of the famous mountain peaks of Europe — *Mont Blanc,* the *Eiger,* the *Matterhorn,* the *Weisshorn,* the *Jungfrau, Piz Palu* and *Grossclockner.* The 1200 glaciers of the Alps are fed from permanent snowlines which vary from 8000 feet (2438m) to 9500 feet (2897m).

Although the range has formed a natural barrier between Italy and the rest of Europe, it has always been comparatively easy to cross thanks to such natural passes as the St Gotthard, the Great and Little St Bernard and the Brenner. It was as early as 218BC that Hannibal made his historic crossing of the Alps, complete with an army and a herd of elephants, to attack the Roman army. Since the twelfth century hospices have been established around the Alpine passes which offer food and shelter to weary travellers.

In the Middle Ages such travellers were usually pilgrims, crossing the Alps en route to Rome, but in later times people began to travel there to explore the mountains themselves. At first this exploration was confined to below the snowline, but eventually it spread beyond as equipment became more sophisticated. By the nineteenth century mountaineering had established itself as a major pastime.

In 1865 Edward Whymper succeeded in climbing the Matterhorn, but his triumph was clouded on the downward journey when one of the party slipped and pulled three others with him. The slender rope snapped and the four tumbled to their deaths leaving Whymper and two others watching, helpless to do anything except spectate as the doomed men frantically clawed for fingerholds as the edge of the precipice loomed larger and larger.

Opposite: *The Eiger,
13,036 feet (4344m), was
first climbed in 1858 by
Charles Barrington, but it
was not until 1961 that a
successful assault was
made in winter. Even
then, the team used the
mountain railway as far as
they could! (ZEFA,
Starfoto)*

Left: *The Matterhorn
(14,701 ft/4900m) has
been eroded by weather
for thousands of years.
This has resulted in its
current, dramatic shape.
(Spectrum Colour
Library)*

Alpinism was established as a popular sport, especially among middle-class Englishmen, and the expansion of the railways and the habit of holidaying encouraged more and more people into the mountains. Today the Alpine slopes are crowded with climbers and skiers and the governments responsible are only now beginning to take measures to protect the flora and fauna of the area.

Politically, the Alps are controlled to a large extent by the Italians: with France in the west, Switzerland in the centre and Austria in the east. Yugoslavia controls the southeast Alps and some of the Bavarian Alps lie in Federal German territory.

The Caucasus

The Alps contain the highest mountains in Europe except for those in the *Caucasus Range,* one of the barriers of Russia and Asia. The whole range lies within USSR territory and is divided into three parts, the most important of which is the Great Caucasus. Bounded by the northern plains of Russia, and in the south by the Black Sea, the Great Caucasus consists of a series of high parallel ridges and contains a great number of glaciers. The permanent snowline varies from 9000 feet (2743m) to 15,000 feet (4572m) at the eastern end.

Exploration was made difficult until about 100 years ago because of the large number of bandit groups that roamed the area. The Czarist government attempted to control the tribes, of which there were, and still are, around 40. Numerous invasions and migrations swept across the mountains in antiquity and in the Middle Ages causing this diversity of population and ethnic background in the Caucasus.

One of the tribes was once under suspicion of murdering two English mountaineers and their guides who were attempting to climb *Koshtan-Tua* in 1889. The four disappeared without

Right: *The Wetterhorn the Bernese Oberland in southwest Switzerland is really a triple peak, the highest of which is 12,15 feet (4051m) high. The first mountaineers used t sleep in the Gleckstein Cave, but this has been replaced by a hut. (ZEFA R. Everts)*

Below: *The Jungfrau (13,653 ft/4419m) was first climbed in 1811 by the Meyer brothers. (Spectrum Colour Library)*

One of the Alpine glaciers. This one, the Aletsch, is the longest of them all and was once described as 'a vast sea of ice'. It is easy to see why. (ZEFA, M. Tjonig)

trace and a local group was heavily suspected by the Russians of having robbed them and disposed of their bodies. A year later this last camp was found, and it was plain that the mountaineers were victims of an accident and not of murder.

The highest mountain in the range is *Elbrus* which rises to 18,481 feet (5633m). It was first climbed by Douglas Freshfield in 1868, the same man who climbed *Kazbek* (16,541 feet/5041m) in the same year.

The area is rich in minerals. Petroleum fields abound in Baku, Grozny and Maikup and there is much manganese, tungsten, molybdenum, copper and coal in Georgia.

Ural Mountains

The other great mountain range of USSR is the Ural, the conventional barrier between Europe and Asia. It extends northwards for 1300 miles (2080km). The highest point is Narodnaja which is 6148 feet (1874m) high.

Unlike other fold mountains, the Urals are remarkably straight, but like the Caucasus the mountains are rich in minerals which were deposited there by the igneous intrusions that accompanied the enormous pressure when the range was formed.

The Urals form a vast watershed between the Volga, Pechora and Ob-Irtysh basins. Among the rivers that rise in the range are the Sovsa, Tura, Iset, Usa, Pechora and the Ural itself. Much of the area is covered with dense forest and so forestry plays an important part in the local economy along with the mining of emeralds.

Other Asian and European ranges

Before we leave the landmass that is Asia and Europe, there are a few more ranges that demand some attention.

The *Kunlun Range* in China used to divide that country from Tibet until Tibet was annexed by her giant northern neighbour. The range extends for about 1000 miles (1600km) and reaches a height of 25,340 feet (7724m) at Ulagh Muztagh. Like most fold ranges Kunlun forms a crescent shape with the western zones compressed and close to each other. At 82° longitude the range divides into two — the *Altyn Tagh* and the *Arka Tagh.*

Other Asian ranges are the *Altai,* which rise to 15,266 feet (4653m); the *Tsinglan Range* in the southern Shensi Province of China and the *Sikhote-Alin* which sprawls along the Russian shore of the Sea of Japan.

Moving back westward, into Eastern Europe, the *Carpathians* stretch from the eastern end of the Alpine range across to the lower Danube. As well as being rich in minerals, the Carpathians are densely forested and are popular tourist attractions for the people of Poland, Czechoslovakia, Hungary and Bulgaria, especially those who do not enjoy good health, as the mountains are rich in mineral springs which are said to be medically beneficial.

The Apennines

The Apennine Range of Italy forms the backbone of that country. It is in the shape of a great arc that extends from the Colle di Cadibona in the north down to the Isole Egade, 870 miles (1392km) to the south. Geologically, the Apennines are linked to the Alps, but geographically, they are quite different. They have no glaciers and no permanent snow. Their average height is around 8000 feet (2438m). The three main divisions are the *North Apennines* which stretch from the Maritime Alps down to Tuscany, the *Central Apennines* from Arezzo to the valley of Pescara, and the *South Appenines* that begin at Pescara and continue down to Cape Apartivento. Whereas the eastern slopes are extremely steep, the Central Apennines are much more gentle, sloping down to plateaus, hills and plains.

The entire range is rich in minerals — iron, tin, copper, and lignite are common. Many classical Italian sculptures

Part of the Caucasus range of USSR. (ZEFA, Dr H. Gärtner)

were carved in Carrara marble and at one time there were 450 quarries being worked between Genoa and Florence to meet the demand for marble.

The range is crossed by numerous roads and ten railways. The famous Autostrada del Sole was completed in 1964 and is the main artery of Italy. The glorious vistas have made the road itself one of the most enjoyable attractions of Italy.

The Pyrenees

The natural barrier between France and Spain is the Pyrenean Range; indeed the contrast between the land on one side of the range and that on the other is so great that it was once said that Europe ends at the Pyrenees. The highest point in the range is *Pico d'Aneto* which rises to 11,168 feet (3404m) and although the range is on the whole much less inspiring than the Alps, the Pyrenees provide far greater difficulty in crossing. There are a few glaciers and the permanent snow-line varies from 8000 to 9000 feet (2438 — 2743m). The range has the highest ice-caves in Europe — the *Grotte Casteret*.

At the Trou du Torro, the Aneto glacier disappears underground and reappears in France as the Garonne river.

Despite their comparative hazards the Pyrenees were crossed by many refugees from Spain to France during the Spanish Civil War and from France to Spain during the Second World War.

Atlas Mountains

It was once said that crossing the Pyrenees into Spain brought one into contact with the hot breath of Africa as the winds blow from that continent,

Right: *Many parts of Norway are extremely mountainous as can be seen from this view of Geirangerfjord. The mountains sweep right down to the sea resulting in one of the most spectacular coastlines of any country in the world. (Spectrum Colour Library)*

Below: *Parts of the Pyrenees have been designated National Park as has this area at Aigues Tortes. (Spectrum Colour Library)*

Below: *Part of the High Atlas range which stretches from Morocco to Tunisia. (ZEFA, K. Helbig)*

across the sea and over the plains of Aragon and Navarre. Indeed the Moors who conquered Spain centuries ago would not have been overawed by the Pyrenees as they would have been familiar with the Atlas Mountains of North Africa.

This range extends over Morocco, Algeria and Tunisia and rises to 13,665 feet (4099m) at Djebel Toubkal. It is divided into several parts. The *High Atlas* extends 400 miles (640km) from Cape Guir towards the Algerian border. The *Middle Atlas* extends northeast

towards the coast and rises to 10,794 feet (3290m) at Djebel Bou Naceur. The *Anti-Atlas* is southwest of the High Atlas. This is an area of broken plateaus and craters, barren plains broken by scattered rocks, walled villages and suspicious mountain folk.

In Algeria the mountains divide into the *Tell Atlas* and the *Saharan Atlas* and the range finishes at Cape Bon in Tunisia. Like most mountain ranges it contains huge deposits of minerals — manganese, lead, zinc, antimony and mercury, all being found there.

For centuries the Atlas mountains remained largely unexplored but recently most of the peaks have been scaled and much survey work has been done by the French.

Ahaggar Mountains

The other major mountain ranges of Africa are the Ahaggar Mountains which are surrounded by the vast arid-ness of the Sahara Desert. Tahat Peak provides the highest point at about 10,000 feet (3048m), but the range is still not completely explored because of its inaccessibility. It is 1000 miles (1600km) south of the Mediterranean, 1000 miles (1610km) east of the Atlantic and 1000 miles (1600km) north of the Bight of Benin. Its position and the searing heat of the Saharan sun combine to make the range an unattractive climb for European mountaineers although French climbers are taking an active interest in it.

Other African ranges

The *Ethiopian Mountains* of Eastern Africa are mainly of volcanic origin and extend over most of Ethiopia, rising to over 15,000 feet (4572m).

The *Virunga Mountains* of East Central Africa are also volcanic. Many of the mountains in the range, including Nyamlagira, are still active. Nyiragongo last erupted in 1948 but the sky above it still glows with the reflected liquid lava at the bottom of the crater.

Right: *As well as being spectacular, the Atlas mountains are rich in valuable minerals such as manganese, lead and zinc. The settlement at the base of the mountains is occupied by Berber tribesmen who, in the twelfth century, swept across North Africa and Spain. (ZEFA, K. Helbig)*

Opposite: *The Ahaggar Mountains in the Sahara Desert are among the most inaccessible in the world being 1000 miles (1600km) from the coast in any direction. (Spectrum Colour Library)*

*The mountains of
Southern Rhodesia.
(ZEFA, J. McGeorge)*

The *Livingstone Mountains* of Tanzania were named after David Livingstone, the Scottish explorer. Lake Malaŵi lies on its western side and the range rises to 7870 feet (2399m) at Chambembe. Much of the range is forested and cultivated and coal is mined.

The *Drakensberg* is the main mountain range of Southern Africa and extends 700 miles (1120km) from eastern Transvaal to Cape Province. Volcanic in origin, the range rises to 11,425 feet (3482m) at Thabantshonyana and much of the area is often covered with snow. The Drakensberg range is said to have

been part of the lost continent of Gondwanland which is supposed to have stretched from South America to Australia. Perhaps it ended at the Great Dividing Range in Australia, which is strung along the eastern seaboard of Australia.

The Great Divide

This range spans 2000 miles (3200km) with its highest point being Mount Kosciusco at 7305 feet (2226m). The range is a vast series of range plateaus. The *Australian Alps* in the south have enormous snowfields. The famous *Blue Mountains* in the north are an elevated

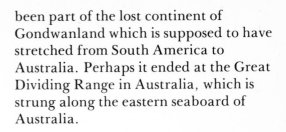

Left: *Table Mountain is one of the most easily recognizable mountains of Africa. (Spectrum Colour Library)*

Below: *The appropriately named Three Sisters are part of the Blue Mountains of Australia. (Spectrum Colour Library)*

crust of red sandstone cut all the way along with huge timbered valleys. North of the Blue Mountains begins a series of mountain forests which extend right up to Cape York. Many rivers rise in the Great Divide and have been utilized by the Australians in the creation of huge hydro-electricity schemes which power the industry and domestic needs of much of eastern Australia.

The Andes

Vast as the Great Divide is, the Andes of South America are even longer. Whereas the Great Divide extends for 2000 miles (3200km), the Andes chain is 5500 miles (8900km) long which is approximately the distance between London and Johannesburg. The Andes is not a single line of formidable peaks, but a succession of parallel and transverse mountain ranges that separate a small western coastal region from the rest of the South American land mass. From the *Patagonian Andes* in the south, the range extends northwards through the *Central Andes, Peruvian Andes, Ecuadorian Andes, Colombian Cordillera* and *Venezuelan Cordillera*. The range begins on a small island off the Tierra del Fuego archipelago — Staten Island — the highest point of which is 3700 feet (1125m).

From here the Patagonian Andes pass through the Isola Grande where all the important ridges — the Darwin, Valdiveso and Sorondo — are less than 7900 feet (2408m) high. The range then rises beyond the Strait of Magellan. As it progresses northwards, it is cut by numerous transverse and longitudinal depressions, many of which are occupied by ice fields, glaciers, rivers, lakes and fjords. The range rises to 11,070 feet (3375m) at Fitzroy and to 11,657 feet (3554m) at Tronodar. The Patagonian Andes

Right: *In Peru, settlements such as this one are built high up in the mountains. (Spectrum Colour Library)*

Below: *Machu Picchu, the site of an ancient Inca city, was discovered hundreds of years after the Inca Empire had been devastated by the Spanish Conquistadors in the sixteenth century. (Spectrum Colour Library, F. Henfield)*

extend to 35°S and are often covered by magnificent forests which reach up to the permanent snowline. The range includes a line of active volcanoes — Yate, Corcovado and Maca — between 40°–45°S.

At around 35°S the Patagonian Andes become the *Central Andes* and undergo a sharp change in character. The width of the range spreads to around 50 miles (80km) and the mountains are higher and more arid. Glaciers are rare and there is little vegetation. Here the Andes divide Chile and Argentina and the last of the volcanoes, Tupangato (22,309 ft/6800m) lies just east of Santiago in Chile.

From there enormous snow cap peak rear up. The highest of these is the highest peak in the western hemispher — Aconcagua. Said to be 22,834 feet (6960m), Aconcagua is swept by

The Rio Negro seen from Argentina. The range rises to a height of 19,815 feet (6400m). (ZEFA, W. Hasenberg)

ferocious winds which make climbing difficult. The mountain was once called the greatest heap of debris in the world and was first climbed in 1897 by a group of Englishmen led by Edward Fitzgerald. Fitzgerald himself failed to reach the summit — he collapsed 1000 feet (305m) from the summit after eating trifle! However his Swiss guide carried on and reached the top. Since then Aconcagua has been climbed many times and there is now a hut at 21,000 feet (6400m). A mule track goes up a further 900 feet (274m), but even so, only one in ten can summon up the energy to climb the last 900 feet (274m). Many other peaks in the Central Andes are over 20,000 feet (6046m) including Bonete, Ojos del Salado and Incahuasi. The range changes character at the peak of Tres Cruces which rises to 20,853 feet (6309m). To the north there is a vast

Part of the Cordillera Blanca in Northwest Peru. (Spectrum Colour Library, F. Henfield)

Left: *The Andean farmers have developed a system of terrace farming that enables them to cultivate the steep slopes of their country. This shows a settlement on an island in Lake Titicaca, the highest lake in the world. (Spectrum Colour Library, F. Henfield)*

plateau called Puna in Argentina and Puna de Atacama in Chile. The Bolivians call it Altiplano. The plateau is bounded by two 'branches' of the Andes, the Occidental and the Oriental. The Altiplano is one of the largest interior basins in the world — 500 miles (800km) long, 80 miles (128km) wide and 11,200 — 12,800 feet (3414 — 3901m) high. In the middle is a great depression which contains Lake Titicaca, the highest navigable lake in the world.

The Cordillera Occidental runs parallel to the coast of Peru forming the beginning of the *Peruvian Andes*. The Cordillera Real from Bolivia ends in the rough mountain pass of Nudo de Vilcanota and from there the Cordillera Carbaya and Vilcanota emerge. The ranges are products of the erosive action of rivers that cut into deep canyons. Traditionally, the Peruvian Andes have been described as three cordilleras which join at Nudo de Vilcanota, forming an immense plateau, 60 miles (96km) wide and 13,000 feet (3962m) high. The Occidental, Central and Oriental Cordilleras run on the Nudo de Pasco. The Occidental is split by the Ca'ejon de Huaylas which separates two ranges, the Cordilleras Blanca and Negra. The Negra contains some of the highest

Below: *Volcanoes are common throughout the Andes. This one in Chile is known as Villarrica. Although it has not erupted for many years, it is still active. (Spectrum Colour Library)*

Opposite: *Skilled engineering and the hard work of hundreds of labourers built this road in Peru, the highest road in the world. (Spectrum Colour Library)*

Below: *The highest mountain of the Eastern Cordillera of the Andes is Mount Illampu 21,275 feet (7000m). (RIDA, H. Boxer)*

Andean peaks including Huascaran at 22,204 feet (6768m). The two ranges join at 9°S.

The Occidental, Central and Oriental Cordilleras run northward into Columbia and end in the Cordillera de Choco. The Central ends at 8°N. Between Central and Occidental Cordilleras is the Patia-Cauca Valley. This is divided into three plains. The southernmost one drains into the Pacific. The middle plain is the highest at 8200 feet (2499m) and the northern plain is the valley of the Cauca.

The *Venezuelan Cordillera* are represented by the Merida which is 280 miles long (443km) and 50-90 miles (80-144km) wide. It begins in Pico el Cobre and ends at Bajada de Lara.

The Andes are composed of thick beds of limestone, sandstone and slate, together with intrusive masses of granitic rocks and enormous quantities of lava. Volcanic activity and earthquakes are still frequent right down the Andean chain.

The range is rich in minerals — gold, silver, copper, zinc and lead — and it

was prospectors for these metals, especially silver and gold, who first explored the range.

The Rocky Mountains

The other great range of the American continent is, of course, the Rocky Mountains of North America, stretching from New Mexico in the south to Alaska in the north. The Rockies represent a vast natural barrier between the east and west of North America. They are made up of around twenty individual ranges. The most southerly mountains of the Rockies are the *Sangre de Cristo* which

themselves are composed of three ranges — the *Sierra Blanca,* the *Culebra* and the *Taos Mountains.* From New Mexico, the *San Juan Mountains* run into Colorado. The range is noted for the extreme beauty of its forested slopes. The highest peak here is Uncompahgre at 14,306 feet (4360m).

North of the San Juan lie the *Sawatch* in western Colorado. Here is Mount Elbert 14,431 feet (4399m) and the Mount of the Holy Cross, so named because of its cross-like formation at the top.

Extending 300 miles (480km) from Colorado Springs is the *Front Range* which is one of the few sources in the

The Grand Tetons of Wyoming and Idaho rise to over 13,000 feet (4000m). A branch of the Rocky Mountains, they are one of the most spectacular examples of fault blocking. (RIDA, P. J. Hill)

world of cryolite, one of the essential ingredients in aluminium making. The Front Range lies to the south of the *Medicine Bow* range and the point at which the two ranges meet is the magnificent Rocky Mountain National Park — one of the most beautiful areas of the American continent.

The next Rocky Mountain range is the *Laramie Mountains* which is the last of the group known as the southern Rockies.

150 miles (240km) east of the Laramies are the *Wind River Mountains* which rise to 13,785 feet (4202m) at Gannett Peak, to the west of the lesser *Wyoming Range*. We then come to the *Uinta Mountains* which swing east to west in a classical fold mountain structure.

North of here are the *Wasatch Mountains* and the *Teton Range* where the famous Yellowstone National Park is situated just to the north. The other boundary of the park is the *Absaroka Range* which runs into northwest Wyoming. At the northern end of the Absarokas, the Rockies swing westwards into the *Madison Range* and then into a range of broken mountains which are different from the rest of the Rockies in that they form a huge granite massif.

The southwest part of the Northern Rockies is made up of the *Bitterroot*

St Mary Lake in the Glacier National Park in Montana. The Great Continental Divide can be seen in the background. (RIDA, D. J. Taylor)

Left: *Mount Athabaska in SW Alberta lies between the Jasper and Banff National Parks. It is 11,452 feet (3800m) high. (RIDA, R. C. L. Wilson)*

Below: *The impressive Mount Hood is in the Cascade Range which spreads from California, through Oregon, Washington and into British Columbia. The range was discovered in 1792 by Vancouver and Broughton. (Spectrum Colour Library)*

Mountains which extend northwards right up to the north end of the Idaho-Montana boundary.

Here the *Lewis Range* forms part of the *Great Continental Divide* which runs northwards through Glacier National Park. This spreads into the Waterton Lakes National Park and the mountains of Alberta in Canada. This area of unparalleled natural beauty was referred to as the 'Backbone of the World' by the Blackfoot Indians.

Appalachian Mountains

The Rockies are on the western coast of America. On the east coast, is a range of mountains 1500 miles (2400km) long known as the Appalachians. They extend south-west from the St Lawrence River in Quebec to the Gulf coastal plain of Alabama. Several different types of land forms are included in the Appalachians: long, narrow, folded ranges separated from each other by narrow valleys; a sharp-crested ridge, the *Blue Mountains,* that extend from Pennsylvania into Georgia along the eastern margin of the Appalachians; gently sloping tablelands that merge in the west with the interior lowlands of the United States; and high forested mountains in New England.

The mountains of the Appalachians are among the most popular holiday and recreational areas in the whole of the United States.

One of the reasons for man's supremacy in the world is his ability to survive and to adapt himself to almost any conditions. It is not surprising therefore that in and around the mountains of the world hundreds of thousands of people of different cultures and tribes have existed successfully and adapted the mountains to their own uses.

Possibly due to the sheer majesty of mountains, and their magnitude and intractability, they have long been regarded as holy places by many people. And so monks of various religions have built temples and shrines on their holy mountains. One Greek mountain is populated entirely by monks, in fact the Greeks call it *Hagion Oros* meaning Holy Mountain. We know it as Mount Athos.

Left: *In Nepal, holy men are often seen sitting beside road-side alters. This altar is dedicated to the Goddess Kali. (ZEFA, G. Heil)*

Below: *The monastery at Vatopedi on Mount Athos in Greece, one of the few remaining theocracies in the world. (Spectrum Colour Library)*

Mount Athos

It is situated on the most easterly of the three tongues of the Chalcidice peninsula of the Aegean Sea and is populated by an autonomous, all-male community. The mountain and its surrounding district is 30 miles (48km) long and 10 miles (16km) across. To visit it, the traveller needs to obtain written permission from the Orthodox Church. The mountain contains 20 monasteries and many hermitages. Despite their rather forbidding appearance the monks are genial and hospitable. They all belong to the Orthodox Christian faith — Greek, Russian, Serbian, Bulgarian and Rumanian — and the mountain is governed by a Holy Assembly of twenty annually elected members. Since 1920

Greece has been the nominal ruler of Athos.

Viewed from afar, the monasteries look like little fortified towns. They are generally built around a small courtyard with richly decorated churches and monks' cells leading into it. In the east part of each of the churches there is a carved screen painted with holy pictures. This divides the church from the sanctuary, where holy relics are stored and where the monks are often found in prayer. Today there are about 3000 monks living on the mountain and a large number of lay brethren. Some of the monasteries are governed by elected committees of monks while others are under the absolute rule of the Abbot.

The former are known as Idiorythmyc and the latter are Cenobian.

Fujiyama

The other famous mountain which was, until recently, an all-male domain was Fujiyama in Japan. For centuries, this volcanic mountain has been sacred to those practising the Shinto religion. It stands 12,389 feet (3776m) high, is permanently snowcapped, and has been described as one of the most beautiful in the world. It was only just over a hundred years ago that women were allowed to go onto Fuji and even today, most expeditions are all-male.

Right: *Mount Fuji in Japan. (ZEFA, D. Schmidt)*

Below: *Much of the livestock on Mount Athos is cared for by lay brethren. Women are forbidden entry into the area. (Spectrum Colour Library)*

Carpathian Mountains

Mountain villages such as this are a common sight in the ranges of Spain. (RIDA, R. T. J. Moody)

However, many millions of ordinary men *and* women live on and around the mountains of the world. The *Carpathians*, for example, have a population density of 180 per square mile (69 per sq.km) with a total population of around 14,000,000. A wide range of

nationalities are represented: Czechs on the western slopes of the Western Carpathians, Poles in the north, Slovaks in the central part and Hungarians in the south. The northern part of the eastern Carpathians is populated by Ukranians. Other groups include Rumanians and Slavs. Many of these peoples are involved in agriculture and forestry. On the

northern slopes rye, oats and potatoes are most commonly grown with maize, sugar beet, grapes and tobacco being found there as well. Above 3000 feet (914m) forestry and pastoral life is the norm. Many of the traditionally agricultural people are now working on the rich reserves of minerals and natural gas that have been found in the region.

The Himalayas

The Himalayas on the other hand are quite sparsely populated. Originally the two main ethnic groups were Indo-Aryan and Mongolian, but successive waves of immigration into the mountains have produced an intermingled population. The Greater Himalayas are

Left: *Two Sherpas on the lower slopes of Annapurna. (RIDA, R. N. Golds)*

Below: *There are many monasteries on the lower slopes of the Himalayas, such as this one at Thyangboche. (RIDA, R. N. Golds)*

generally populated by Mongolian-type people and the Lesser Himalayas are the home of Indo-Aryans. One of the Indo-Aryan tribes is the Gaddis. The Gaddis are essentially a hill people owning huge flocks of sheep and herds of goats which they bring down from the upper pasture in winter when conditions become impossible. Another related tribe is the Gutar which is comprised of migrating pastoral people who wander from area to area with their flocks and herds.

On the northern slopes of the Himalayas are the Champa who follow a nomadic life in the Upper Indus valley, the Ladakhi, an agrarian people who

have settled on the terraces that flank the Indus in Kashmir, and the Islamic Balti peoples.

In the Nepalese Himalayas are the Newars, Tamangs, Gurungs, Magas, Sherpas and Kirats, who were the earliest inhabitants of the Nepal valley. The Gurungs live on the southern slopes of Annapurna and pasture their cattle as high as 12,000 feet (3658m). Perhaps the most famous representative of the Sherpas is Sherpa Tenzing who stood on the summit of Everest along with Edmund Hillary, the first two men ever to be there.

Other ethnic tribes, such as the Akas and Tanis, of the Himalayas wander from area to area, growing crops on the

Below: *As well as men and women, there is a great deal of wildlife in the Himalayas. This fox was photographed in the Himalayan foothills. (RIDA, R. N. Golds)*

Right: *A Tibetan monk in Nepal. (ZEFA, B. Leidmann)*

Left: Herds of yaks are often cared for by Nepalese shepherds, moving the herd on from one grazing area to another. (Spectrum Colour Library)

Below: Collecting the harvest in the French Alps. (Spectrum Colour Library)

land and moving on when they have used up the goodness of the soil. This practice is known as shifting cultivation.

The Alps

Perhaps the most famous mountain culture is the Alpine which spreads through Switzerland, France, Italy, Germany, Austria and Yugoslavia. Cattle and agricultural produce form the centre of Alpine folk life. This is because the high cool mountain valleys are unsuitable for cultivation but will support cattle and dairy farming, whereas the larger, wetter, sunnier lower valleys are ideal for agricultural produce.

Seasonal movement of cattle is common because during the summer when the snowline recedes, herds are moved up mountain to take advantage of the lush pasture which appears under the snow. When winter comes and conditions are impossible, the herds are

moved down mountain to winter grazing areas. Johanna Spyri's book, *Heidi,* has painted a noble portrait of poor people living simply and independently on the Alps. This has some basis in fact. There is an old Alpine saying, 'Mountain dwellers only cooperate when they have to; and they have to a lot.' Alpine children can still be seen playing with simply-made wooden toys, and dressed in traditional clothes. Candles are still in common use and potstone stoves are not unusual.

The centre of each alpine village is the parish church, with the family forming the centre of social life. The society is very much male-oriented with son following father in the traditional occupations and mother teaching daughter to play a slightly subservient role. As soon as they are able to do so, children are required to help with chores, carrying meals to the shepherds, helping in the house and later, tending to the herds. At twelve, boys and girls are considered to be full-fledged farm hands.

When children get married, their parents lend them land and cattle. This is taken into account on the death of the parents when parental land and possessions are divided amongst the family.

Below: *In winter, when these pastures are covered in snow, animals will be taken to lower slopes. (RIDA, R. C. L. Wilson)*

Right: *Typical Swiss chalets on the lower slopes of the Wetterhorn. (ZEFA, Dr W. Fühler)*

Wooden houses are still common throughout the Alps and the houses can combine living area, barn and stable.

Although the tourist industry in some ways threatens the traditional alpine way of life it perhaps encourages new generations to stay in the area and to carry on their traditional crafts and skills.

The Andes

At the other side of the world, in the Andes, in South America, shepherds also eke out a living on the high-altitude slopes, but because of the lack of oxygen there, the mountains are sparsely populated. There is a mining industry,

Right: *Peruvian peasants on the shores of Lake Titicaca. (ZEFA, Janoud)*

Below: *Llamas. (Spectrum Colour Library)*

of course, but the greater part of the Andean population is dedicated to agriculture and raising sheep, goats, llamas and alpacas. Traditional crafts of the mountain folk include ceramics and weaving.

The Rocky Mountains and Appalachians

In the Rocky and Appalachian mountains of North America there are still a few traditional mountain people who live up to the Hollywood image of sturdy, independent folk dedicated to the land on which they live. Despite the appalling poverty in which they live, a distinctive culture has evolved with handicrafts, ballads, and a rich folklore which although not typical of mountain people everywhere does characterise the struggle which such people have had to eke out a living from the mountains of the world.

Left: *Weaving is a common craft among Andean people. Shawls, as well as being warm, are used by the women for carrying their children. (RIDA, H. Boxer)*

Below: *A Peruvian shepherdess. (RIDA, H. Boxer)*

Mountain sports

There are two major sports associated with mountains. One involves climbing up them — mountaineering; the other involves coming down them — skiing.

Skiing

In the Norwegian Ski Museum in Oslo there is a rock carving that is at least 4000 years old. It was found in the Arctic Circle and shows two men travelling across the land with sticks of wood attached to their feet. It is the earliest record of skiers in the world.

Originally skiing was a means of travelling across snow-covered land and probably originated in Scandinavia. Indeed, cross-country skiing is still referred to as Nordic skiing. Skiing down mountainsides for the sheer exhilaration of watching the landscape whizz past, for the joy of feeling the cold air rush against the face and for the challenge of trying to ski faster than one's rivals was a natural extension of cross-country skiing. The first skiing competition was held in 1767 when Norwegian troops skied for prizes of money. This, of course, was a Nordic event, but in the 1860s

Left: Once atop a mountain, the climber has time to appreciate the spectacular view. Faced with views as spectacular as this, it is no wonder that mountaineering is such a popular sport. (Spectrum Colour Library)

Below: Skiing in the Austrian Alps. (ZEFA, Prof Hoppichler)

competitive downhill skiing was established in California. The competitors used wooden skis that were 12 feet (3.6m) long.

Interest in skiing and ski competition grew rapidly and in 1879 10,000 people, including the king of Norway, watched the first ski-jump competition which was held at Huseby Hall in Oslo. Eighteen years later, a group of five Germans skied down the slopes of the peaks of the Bernese Oberland. Other spectacular feats followed. Such skiing was known as ski mountaineering, as, before the men could come down the mountainsides on skis, they had to carry their equipment to the top of the slopes, using ropes, ice picks and other conventional mountaineering equipment.

Since then downhill skiing — Alpine skiing — has increased in popularity at an amazing rate. Wherever there is a snow-covered slope there are skiers on it. Initially the prerogative of the 'idle rich', skiing as a sport has now spread to every stratum of society. The Alps still have a magnetism of their own, but in Greece, Yugoslavia, Norway, Scotland, Australia, New Zealand, Cyprus, the United States, Canada, Spain, France, — anywhere that there is a steep slope covered in snow — someone will be skiing down it.

Technology has worked to the advantage of the skier. No longer does he or she have to struggle up a mountainside, skis over shoulder, sticks in hand and haversack on back. Today there are ski tows, cable cars and ski lifts. Restaurants have been built to cater for the needs of the inner man. Trained instructors are on hand to teach those who cannot ski and to help improve the technique of those who can. Aircraft carry enthusiasts from city to ski-slope. A whole industry has cashed in on the supposed glamour of skiing. Valleys that were once quiet and inaccessible now play host to thousands of enthusiasts. Huge hotels stand where once there were a few houses. Expensive restaurants sell exotic dishes where once the village café stood.

All this has affected the mountains and the mountain people. There are species of flora and fauna which are in danger of extinction. For example, the once prolific Eidelweiss of the Alps is now a protected plant. Some animals have been forced higher and higher up the mountainside to a habitat and conditions not natural to them. Traditional skills that were once handed down from father to son are now in danger of fading for ever. Whereas, son was once happy to follow father in looking after the family farm, and daughter was happy to do as her mother and grandmother had done for generations, they are now tempted by the hotels and restaurants and the very different world of the skiers from far away.

Skiing techniques and equipment have been greatly modified since the early days. Fashion in the length of skis has varied from year to year, but one thing has remained constant. Those who love the mountains and who love skiing have always been determined that safety comes first — safety for the skier and safety for the environment.

In 1924 the Fédération Internationale de Ski was founded and is today the world governing body of the sport. All national ski associations are affiliated to it and as these are made up of local clubs, the FIS influences all facets of the sport.

The first ski club was set up in Trysil in Norway as long ago as 1861. The first one in the United States was founded in Berlin, New Hampshire in 1872 and the Ski Club of Great Britain was established in 1903.

Today, skiing is an Olympic event and has been since 1924, when the first Winter Olympic Games were held at Chamonix in France, although Alpine skiing was not included until 1936 when the Games were held at Garmisch-Partenkirchen in Germany.

There are three Alpine events; downhill, slalom and giant slalom. For the downhill, the course is usually between 1.5 miles (2.4km) and 3 miles (5km) and a vertical descent of 729 yards (800m) and 912 yards (1000m) is usually prescribed. Average speeds vary from 40-50 miles (64-80km) per hour.

The slalom was first initiated by Sir

Modern technology has made life much easier for the skier. Rather than carrying his skis to the top of the slopes, he is now pulled up on ski tows or carried up on chair lifts. (ZEFA, Prof Hoppichler)

Alfred Lunn in the early 1920s. The course is a series of 'gates' marked by pairs of flags through which the skier must pass. In the men's competition there are usually 55 to 75 gates on a vertical descent of around 183 yards (200m). In the women's competition there are usually 40 to 60 gates.

The giant slalom has characteristics of both the downhill and the slalom. The gates are wider apart and the course is much longer than the ordinary slalom. It is perhaps the most popular of the three as a spectator sport, no doubt because of the spectacular (but relatively painless) falls and spills that can occur. Also, the sight of a skier swooshing downhill, weaving in and out of the slalom gates, is one of the most elegant and exciting of all sports from the watchers' point of view.

Mountaineering

The sport to which mountains have given their name is, of course, mountaineering. Climbing mountains was not always a sport. The first attempts to climb mountains were motivated by the desire to find out if gods and dragons lived on the peaks, to build altars, to survey one's country from a great height and to make scientific observations.

As a sport, mountaineering began to develop about 150 years ago when English, French and German climbers were attracted to the Alps simply for the sake of climbing them. Although mountaineering is a team effort, it is the ultimate sporting challenge of one man pitting his wits against nature. The climber must rely on his own powers of physical endurance and his own judgment. It is a test of courage, cunning, strength, resourcefulness, ability and stamina.

But the true beginnings of mountaineering go back to 1760 when a young Swiss, Horace-Bénédict de Saussure, first looked at Mont Blanc and vowed that if he did not climb it first, he would be responsible in some way for its ascent. He offered prize money for the first climb, but it was not claimed until 1786

Right: To achieve this degree of skill on skis takes many years of hard work and practice. (ZEFA, H. Schmied)

Opposite: Mountaineering is, essentially, based on teamwork. The leader is responsible for forging ahead up the mountain and the men below him are responsible for ensuring that if he slips, they will do all in their power to break his fall. Once the front man has reached safety, the onus lies on him to ensure that the others reach their destination. (ZEFA, Ung. Fotostudio)

when Mont Blanc was scaled by Michel Gabriel Paccard. In 1787, de Saussure himself climbed the peak.

By the middle of the 19th century, groups of British climbers and their continental guides were making a determined assault on the Alps and by 1870 all the major peaks had been scaled. Attention turned to finding more complex routes to the top and by the end of the century attention was turning to other ranges — the Andes, the Rockies and the Himalayas.

Throughout the 20th century all the major peaks were eventually climbed and today the emphasis is again on finding new and more difficult routes. Faces that were once considered to be unclimbable are now scaled with comparative ease, thanks to the technical

Climbing glaciers is one of the most challenging aspects of mountaineering. Specially-designed mountain boots ensure a safe grip for the feet and the ice picks give the mountaineer a safe anchor while he moves upward. Note that the axes are put into the ice below arm level. This is because it is easier to gain height by pushing down on the arms, rather than pulling up on them. (John Cleare)

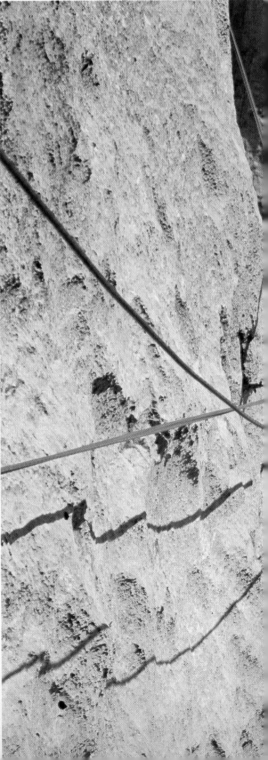

The front man has gone ahead and secured ropes onto the mountain face. Other members of an expedition use these ropes as handholds. The black rope is secured to the next man up the rock face so that if the climber loses his grip he will be saved from falling. (ZEFA, T. Hiebeler)

advances that have been applied to mountaineering equipment. No longer do climbers pack a haversack, pick up an alpinstock or ice axe and set off.

Expeditions are planned in extraordinary detail. The equipment used would be unrecognizable to the nineteenth-century pioneers. Ropes, hammers, boots, pulleys, rope ladders, pitons, have all been developed to an amazing degree of sophistication.

Today's ropes are generally made of artificial fibre which is stronger than natural jute. The thickness is usually about ½ inch (1.25cm) and lengths of 130 feet (40m) are normally carried.

It is the job of the leader of the party (usually the most experienced) to climb first. If he slips, it is up to the second to break his fall by playing the rope. The leader will drive pitons (pegs) into cracks in the rocks for two reasons: they provide extra support where there are few handholds and ropes can be attached to them by means of a karabiner. This is a ring that opens and shuts with a strong spring

action, through which the rope is threaded. Thus, if the leader slips, his fall can be minimized. If there are no cracks suitable to take the pitons, holes can be drilled in the rock face with special stone drills. Fissures that are too large to take a piton can be reduced with wood or plastic chocks.

Because mountaineering is a combination of three types of climbing, the amount of equipment can vary from expedition to expedition. The three stages are hillwalking, rock climbing and ice climbing. For climbing such a mountain as the Eiger, the equipment would have to include, the mallets, pitons, ropes and hooks essential for rock climbing as well as crampons, ice axes, ice pitons and ice screws.

Once the summit has been reached, the mountaineers have to come down again. This can be as difficult as the ascent. A cliff which has been scaled may be impossible to descend because of overhangs. Such obstacles are overcome by a technique known as abseiling. The climbing rope is wound round the overhang or put through a piton. The climber arranges the rope round the inside of one thigh, round his shoulders and then round his other thigh. He then slides down using his feet to kick himself off the rock face.

The dangers of mountaineering are often exaggerated. Spectacular climbing accidents tend to be splashed across the headlines of the world's newspapers, but well-trained climbers with good judgment climb for many years. Many accidents involve the ill-trained and badly equipped who do not respect the mountain and who are not physically or mentally ready to climb.

It is ironic that Dougal Haston a well-known Scottish mountaineer, who cheated death many times while climbing, was killed on the mountains. It was not climbing, however, that killed him, but skiing.

As long as there are mountains people will want to climb them. The challenge of the mountains has always been met by those exceptional few who are fired with a lust for adventure that only the mountains can satisfy.

A few facts

Opposite: *The climber in this picture is coming down the north face of the Matterhorn. The rope gives him a handhold as he uses his feet to move down the ice face. (John Cleare)*

Right: *Mount Ararat. (Spectrum Colour Library)*

The highest mountain in the world is Mount Everest in the Himalayas. It rises to 29,154 feet (8848m) and was first climbed in 1953.

Until 1832 the highest mountain was thought to be Dhaulagiri, also in the Himalayas. It is 26,810 feet (8172m) and was first climbed in 1960.

Annapurna III (24,858 feet/7577m) was the first major peak to be climbed by an all-female party when a group of Japanese women climbed it in 1970.

Mount Ararat in Turkey (16,945 feet/ 5165m) was not climbed until 1829, despite the fact that Noah is said to have brought the Ark to rest there, thousands of years earlier.

The highest peak in the western hemisphere is Aconcagua in Argentina which is 22,834 feet (6960m) high.

Huascaran in Peru (22,204 feet/6768m high) was the first major peak to be scaled by a woman on her own — the American, Annie Peck in 1908.

The highest peak in North America is Mount McKinley in Alaska. It is 20,032 feet (6194m) high.

The highest active volcano in the world is Cotapaxio in Ecuador. Its height is 19,347 feet (5897m).

Kilimanjaro in Tanzania is the highest peak in Africa, being 19,340 feet (5895m) high.

Below: *Mount Cook. (Spectrum Colour Library)*

Right: *Kilimanjaro.*
(ZEFA, G. Heil)

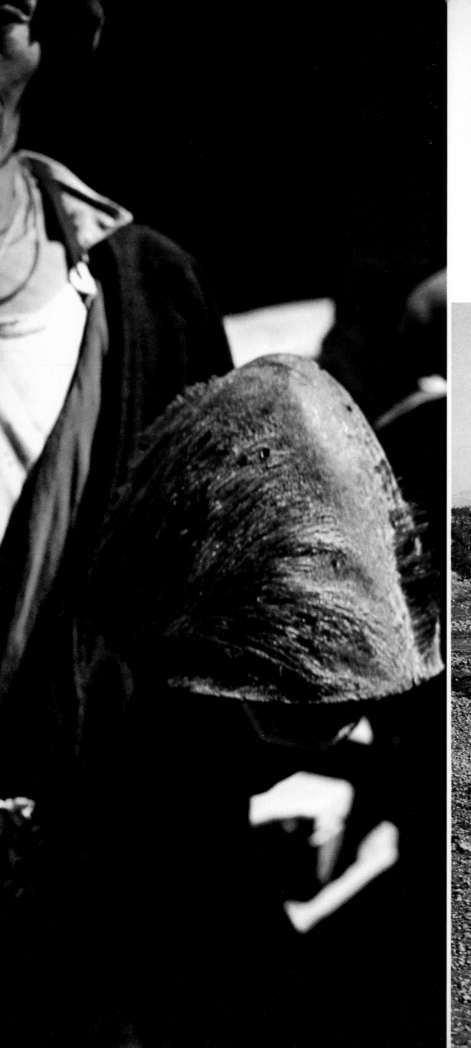

The highest peak in Russia is Communist Peak (24,590 feet/7495m).

The highest mountain in western Europe is Mont Blanc. 15,771 feet (4807m) high, it was first climbed in 1786.

Mauna Kea in Hawaii (13,796 feet/4205m high) is the highest island mountain in the world.

The highest mountain in New Zealand is Mount Cook at 12,349 feet (3764m) high.

Britain's highest peak is Ben Nevis in Scotland at 4406 feet (1343m).

Mount Athos in Greece is forbidden to women and has the largest concentration of monasteries of any area in the world.

Mount Everest is said to be the home of the Abominable Snowman. Although there is no evidence of its existence, not one of the expedition that went to trace it in 1968 was willing to say that it does not exist.

The first recorded men to die while attempting to climb Mount Blanc were three guides in an expedition in 1820.

The most famous 19th century mountaineer, Edward Whymper, did not intend to become a mountaineer at all. He first visited the Alps to make sketches for a publishing firm.

When Mount Kelod in Java erupted, *38,000,000* tons of water and lava poured down the mountainside killing 5100 people.

Endpapers: *In the Atlas mountains, villages are often built on peak-tops; they are easier to defend. (ZEFA, R. Everts)*

Opposite: *A reconstruction of what is thought to be the scalp of a Yeti (Abominable Snowman). (RIDA, D. J. Taylor)*

Below: *Ben Nevis. (Spectrum Colour Library)*